CELEBRATE JESUS

THE CHRISTMAS STORY THROUGH THE EYES OF AN ANGEL

CHARLES R. SWINDOLL

THOMAS NELSON
Since 1798

NASHVILLE DALLAS MEXICO CITY RIO DE JANEIRO BEIJING

Published in Nashville, Tennessee, by Thomas Nelson. Thomas Nelson is a registered trademark of Thomas Nelson, Inc.

Published in association with Yates & Yates, www.yates2.com

Thomas Nelson, Inc. titles may be purchased in bulk for educational, business, fund-raising, or sales promotional use. For information, please e-mail SpecialMarkets@ThomasNelson.com.

Unless otherwise identified, Scripture quotations used in the Gabriel story are from The New American Standard Bible® (NASB). © 1960, 1962, 1963, 1971, 1972, 1973, 1975, 1977, and 1995 by the Lockman Foundation, La Habra, California. All rights reserved. Used by permission. (www.Lockman.org) Scripture quotations used in the Advent readings are from the HOLY BIBLE: NEW INTERNATIONAL VERSION® . © 1973, 1978, 1984 by International Bible Society. Used by permission of Zondervan Publishing House. All rights reserved.

ISBN: 978-1-4002-8054-4

Printed in the United States of America

08 09 10 11 12 BTY 8 7 6 5 4 3 2 1

In the sixth month, God sent the angel Gabriel to Nazareth, a town in Galilee, to a virgin pledged to be married to a man named Joseph . . . The angel went to her and said, "Greetings, you who are highly favored! The Lord is with you."

*God's promises
always exceed
expectations.*

GABRIEL

I know more than any mortal could, for I stand in the very presence of God and announce His decrees to people on earth. Yet, despite the timeless, heavenly perspective I enjoy as one of His heavenly messengers, one particular mystery is beyond my ability to understand: God's persistent, unrelenting love for people. It began before time and it will never end.

My specific role was to carry announcements concerning the Messiah, which I first revealed to God's servant Daniel. He lived more than five hundred years before the Messiah was to be born, during the reign of Belshazzar of Babylon. I had to do battle and overcome the forces of evil to reach the prophet, and when I arrived, I interpreted the visions he had received. I described the political events that would signal the coming of the Messiah along with a detailed timetable so that no one could overlook his arrival.

As instructed, Daniel kept his prophecy from the general public at the time, but recorded every detail in a scroll for future generations. He also shared his revelation with the king's astrologers and magicians, even going so far as to calculate the future position of the constellations when the Messiah was to be born. Long after he was dead, long after the people of Judah had returned from exile, he anticipated and predicted the skies would signal the arrival of the King of the Jews.

World events unfolded exactly as they had been revealed to Daniel. The Babylonians gave way to the Persians, who were, in turn, conquered by the Greeks. Then the Romans became the rulers of Judea. The decree of Artaxerxes to rebuild the wall of Jerusalem established the time in which the people of Israel could expect to receive their king. And as the heavenly clock wound down, I thought, *Certainly, after all that I had announced—the signs, the times, the most explicit details recorded by Daniel—certainly, the people of Judah would be*

watching and waiting. Certainly, they would have no trouble recognizing their need for a savior. Certainly, they would anticipate and celebrate the arrival of their deliverer. Everything had been revealed. All the people of Israel had to do was watch the calendar, travel to Bethlehem as the prophet Micah later announced, and welcome Him.

But I am not omniscient. I could not see the future as God does. As the time approached, His covenant people didn't appear ready, which confused me greatly. But, as always, He had a plan. Knowing that Israel

would be distracted or disinterested, He promised a forerunner through His prophet Malachi. As the time for the Messiah ripened, He sent me on a mission. I was now to announce the birth of the forerunner of the Christ to a priest in Jerusalem.

When I appeared to Zacharias, the father of the boy, I was excited beyond words. The plan announced more than five hundred years earlier was about to commence! I told the old man that he and his aging wife would give birth to John, the forerunner before the Christ, and that

he would serve God in the spirit and power of Elijah. But, to my utter dismay, he resisted my message. He failed to believe me!

Did every Jew think that Israel was like an aged woman, too old to bear new life? Did they not understand that *God can do anything?!*

While I looked with sorrow on Zacharias for his failing hope, I admit that I bristled at his lack of faith. And by God's instruction, I struck him deaf and mute for the duration of Elizabeth's pregnancy. He would be a

living symbol of Israel's failure. As a priestly nation to the world, it was their duty to proclaim God's Word and become an example of belief.

I returned to the throne room of heaven entirely dejected and confided in a fellow angel, "I know God's plans never fail, but I fear this plan will not go as smoothly as I had anticipated." The next phase worried me even more.

God explained that the Messiah must be born of a virgin.

"Why a virgin?" I asked.

"Because He is to be My Son," He replied.

This took me by surprise, and I began to see that His plan involved far more than delivering Israel from the oppression of Rome, more than giving them political power and economic prosperity, more than merely fulfilling the promise of land to Abraham. I should have known the character of God better, having served Him as long as I had. His promises *always* exceed expectations.

He continued, "I announced My plan soon after the

fall of Adam and Eve in the Garden. But don't fault yourself for failing to notice. Even Moses, who recorded My words, did not realize their full meaning. If you recall, I pronounced a series of curses as a consequence of disobedience. I cursed the woman to suffer anguish during childbirth. I cursed the man to toil for his sustenance. I cursed their intimacy to endure strife. I cursed the ground to produce weeds and thorns along with crops. But do you remember the first curse I pronounced?"

"Yes," I replied. "You cursed the serpent who deceived them to crawl upon the ground, and that, one day, the heel of her seed would crush his head."

The Lord God nodded in approval. "Yes, but you omitted a part."

"Do you mean where You said the serpent would bruise the heel of her seed?"

"Indeed, I promised that the offspring of the woman would destroy evil forever, but not without great personal cost. You see, My plan has always been to

save humankind from the affliction of evil."

"But, Lord," I asked, "can You not rid the world of evil simply by destroying Satan and all his angels?"

"No. Unfortunately, when the first man chose to disobey, he became infected with the disease of evil. And he passed it on to the next generation, and they to the next, so that all of humankind is inseparably bound to evil. To destroy all evil, I would have to destroy the people I have made, the people I love so very, very much."

As I thought about the problem of sin and evil, I realized the difficulty. Transgression of God's Laws—decrees that reflect His very character—must carry a penalty or they are meaningless. To forgive the sin without penalty would require God to deny His very character. Yet to eradicate sin would destroy the sinner.

Unable to resolve the dilemma, I asked, "How will You destroy sin and preserve the people?"

The Lord God glowed with pleasure at the

opportunity to reveal the next detail of His plan. "I will provide a substitute—someone to pay the penalty of sin on their behalf."

"But who?" I protested. "How can someone pay for the sins of another if he dies paying for his own?"

"A very astute question," He answered. "The substitute must not have *any* sin of his own."

I was even more perplexed. "But Lord, the substitute would have to be a human in order to represent humanity, yet all of humanity has been infected with

evil. Furthermore, this substitute would have to be superhuman in order to pay the penalty for all people, to die a death that would cover not just one sinner's penalty, but that of the whole multitude! What substitute can possibly suffice?"

After a short silence, God said, "God."

I stood dumbfounded. It didn't seem possible. And if it were, it didn't seem fair. Indeed, it wasn't! This was grace. So characteristic of Him, yet utterly beyond my ability to comprehend.

He continued, "I will send My eternal Son to be the Messiah. He will be the substitute. The Messiah will not be the son of a sinful, earthly father, but My Son, born of a virgin to preserve His sinlessness. The Messiah will be man. The Messiah will be God. Being the God-man, He will represent humankind, yet He will have no sin. Furthermore, after He dies on behalf of all humankind, He will conquer death by rising from the grave."

I could not speak. The perfection of His plan—so ingenious, so simple, so intricate—left me even more

amazed than seeing Him create the universe with a mere word.

"Do you see now?" He asked. "The first curse I pronounced in the Garden—the curse in which the woman's offspring would suffer the sting of evil—was a curse upon the Almighty. The Father will suffer the loss of His Son, who will suffer an excruciating death, matched only by His abandonment to suffering by the Spirit."

At this, I wept. The immense love of God was more than I could fathom. The selfless grace of God was

beyond my comprehension. And for what? Creatures who neither desired Him nor sought Him, who not only failed to believe but who refused to believe. This will always remain a mystery to me.

As I considered how He would implement His plan, how the Messiah would be born of a virgin, I noted that it would bring incredible hardship on the chosen couple. It would call for unqualified obedience, complete submission. I humbly asked, "Can any such people be found in all of Judea or Galilee?"

"Yes," He said. "In fact, that is your next task. You are to go to a devout young woman, a virgin, who is betrothed to a spiritually sensitive young man. I have prepared them since childhood for this. They have been reared by godly parents and are therefore faithful students of My Word who earnestly desire to obey. The young woman is Mary. Go to her now. Tell her that she will be the mother of the Messiah."

"What about the young man?" I asked.

"Not now. I have much to teach him first. I will use

this ordeal to prepare Joseph for the difficult task of rearing the Son of God."

I pitied the man for what he was about to endure. "Is there no easier way?" I asked.

"You already know the answer to that. Don't worry. I have a man waiting for him in Jerusalem. When Joseph's heart is soft, when he is ready to hear and accept My will, My servant Simeon will be there to guide him. Then he will be able to receive the announcement from you. Now, go."

I delighted to tell the young woman. Naturally, she was confused at first, but she never hesitated to obey. And while she fully understood the hardship it would bring, she saw it as the most wonderful honor any woman could receive. Her attitude and obedience qualified her for angelic service. But it was better that she was created for this purpose.

To help Mary endure the loneliness of misunderstanding until Joseph was ready, the Lord arranged for her to visit Elizabeth, whose heart He had

prepared. In the meantime, I waited for the Lord's signal before appearing to Joseph in a dream. I knew he would be the greater challenge. It was a particular relief to me when I could assure him that Mary had not betrayed his love. And he, like Mary, never hesitated to obey the Lord God, despite the lifetime of difficulties it was sure to bring.

As the time approached for Mary to deliver the Christ, heaven could barely contain the excitement, so I was distressed by the response of people on earth.

Elizabeth's unusual pregnancy and Zacharias's experience in the temple caused a sensation in the Judean hill country, yet very few anticipated the Messiah. The teachers of Scripture in the temple had certainly seen the prophecies of Isaiah, Daniel, Micah, and Malachi, yet no one truly sought the Christ. Bad enough that he would be delivered in a stable and cradled in a feeding trough, but the King of all creation was about to be born, and no one knew.

This was a mystery that would lead me to learn

another lesson about God's plan. And it began with my next mission. I was to lead a contingent of several thousand angels to announce the Savior's birth to—of all people—shepherds.

The only class of people considered lower than shepherds were thieves. Even Gentiles were afforded more respect. Again, I found myself baffled by God's logic. Were the plan mine, I would have roused the sleeping world by trumpeting the birth of the Messiah in the temple and in the royal courts. I would have engaged the important people in welcoming the new King to earth. I would have caused a supernatural, dazzling, cosmic display to coincide with His birth so everyone would know that God had come from the heavens to earth in the form of human flesh.

But not God. He said, "I will announce the birth of the Savior only to those who care to know it, only to those looking for a savior. Those who want a king to lead them into battle or a leader to make them rich will not know what to do with My Anointed One. If the rich

and the learned and the powerful care to find Him, they will have no trouble. I have made the time and place of His birth known to all mankind for many centuries."

So I found a small band of shepherds tending sheep in the fields within an hour's walk of Bethlehem. Once the Savior was born, I approached them quietly so as not to startle them too much, and then once I had their attention, I split the veil between Earth and heaven to reveal a host of angels praising God. And those Bedouins responded exactly as I had hoped. They leapt

to their feet and joined the praise of heaven, then immediately set out to find the Christ in Bethlehem.

As the Lord God carried out His plan, I began to see an important truth. Not every heart is prepared to receive a savior, or to recognize Him when He arrives. And this saddened me. In heaven, our entire existence revolves around the adoration of God, and every activity is a response to His perfect will. I cannot imagine living any other way. Humans pursue happiness and fulfillment apart from Him. Some even think that

communion with God will mean the end of personal satisfaction. Most are barely aware that sin has separated them from the source of their contentment and continue to live in vain pursuit of cheap substitutes.

I suppose nothing has changed very much since Adam's tragic choice so long ago.

I was briefly encouraged by the response of the shepherds, but I soon fell into a deep despondency. God noticed the sorrow on my face and asked me to share my heart with Him.

"I don't understand, Lord," I sobbed. "The greatest event in all of human history has just taken place, an act of grace too wonderful for words, yet almost no one cared to notice. You know all things. You can see what I cannot. Please, tell me, is there any hope for humankind? You have sent the Savior. Will any receive Him?"

I felt the compassion of God envelope me as He answered. "Gabriel, My faithful champion, your concern for humanity reflects My own. Come, let Me show you something that will surely warm your heart as it does

Mine. Look there in the temple. Do you see someone familiar?"

"Simeon. The old man you sent to instruct Joseph."

"He's there almost every day. I made him a promise years ago that he would not die before laying eyes on the Messiah. There are many more just like him all over the world, though not all of them know it yet. They long to see the Savior and they faithfully go to their respective temples looking for Him. Soon they will see Him. Soon they will hear."

"Will all of them respond like Simeon? Will they receive the Savior?" I asked with eagerness.

"No. Not nearly as many as you would wish. But many will. Multitudes, in fact. And not only in Judea and Galilee. Look."

He directed my attention to a spot on the eastern side of the Arabian desert. There, a cloister of Magi preserved the traditions of the Babylonian and Persian astrologers. As they looked into the western sky, high above the horizon, a new light triggered a memory.

One of the magicians dug out an old manuscript and rediscovered Daniel's calculations. And after comparing his charts to the sky, he searched the Hebrew Scriptures for the significance of Daniel's map of the stars.

He soon found his answer. A king! But not just any king. The King of the Jews. A King who would eventually rule the world.

The Magi knew that a delegation must be sent to investigate, so they elected a number of representatives and assembled an expedition to Jerusalem. (Where else would they expect to find a king than in the capital city?) They traveled more than three months to see the new King, and when they found Him, they did something extraordinary. They fell down on their faces and worshiped!

Unfortunately, not everyone responded to the news of Christ so favorably. The Magi inadvertently stirred Herod's jealousy, which led to a hunt for the Christ child, not to worship Him but to destroy Him. His ruthless search led to the mass murder of male infants

throughout the region, but the Lord God sent me to warn Joseph. I instructed him to take his little family to Egypt for safety, where they would live for no less than three years. Then I was there to summon him home to Galilee after Herod had died. But just to be on the safe side, Joseph elected to settle in Nazareth instead of Cana. In the seclusion of the little forgotten town, he would ply his trade, teach Yeshua all that he knew about the Law, the Prophets, and the Writings, and look for the day when he could explain that He was adopted.

As the boy grew in wisdom, stature, and in favor
with God and men, I saw the drama that played out in
Bethlehem repeated again and again. Most ignored Him,
many rejected Him, some recognized the Savior and,
like the Magi, fell down and worshiped.

In time, I came to understand the grand truth
behind God's plan. Those who want a Savior will find
Him. And if they see Him as He is, they will worship.

My great hope for the sake of humanity is that wise
men will continue to seek Him.

25 DAYS OF ADVENT SCRIPTURES

This Christmas season, during Advent when we anticipate the birth of our Lord and Savior Jesus Christ, read through these Scriptures with your family and reflect on how God's promises always exceed expectations.

First Sunday of Advent, November 30, 2008

ISAIAH 9:2, 6–7

The people walking in darkness

    have seen a great light;

    on those living in the land of the shadow of death

    a light has dawned . . .

For to us a child is born,

    to us a son is given,

    and the government will be on his shoulders.

    And he will be called

Wonderful Counselor, Mighty God,
Everlasting Father, Prince of Peace.
Of the increase of his government and peace
there will be no end.
He will reign on David's throne
and over his kingdom,
establishing and upholding it
with justice and righteousness
from that time on and forever.
The zeal of the LORD Almighty
will accomplish this.

First Monday of Advent, December 1, 2008

ISAIAH 1:18

"Come now, let us reason together,"
     says the LORD.
   "Though your sins are like scarlet,
     they shall be as white as snow;
     though they are red as crimson,
     they shall be like wool."

_____

_____

_____

_____

_____

_____

_____

_____

_____

_____

_____

_____

First Tuesday of Advent, December 2, 2008

ISAIAH 25:8–9

He will swallow up death forever.

   The Sovereign LORD will wipe away the tears

   from all faces;

   he will remove the disgrace of his people

   from all the earth.

   The LORD has spoken.

In that day they will say,

   "Surely this is our God;

we trusted in him, and he saved us.
This is the LORD, we trusted in him;
let us rejoice and be glad in his salvation."

_____

_____

_____

_____

_____

_____

_____

_____

_____

_____

_____

_____

_____

_____

_____

_____

_____

First Wednesday of Advent, December 3, 2008

ISAIAH 42:6-7

"I, the LORD, have called you in righteousness;
   I will take hold of your hand.
   I will keep you and will make you
   to be a covenant for the people
   and a light for the Gentiles,
   to open eyes that are blind,
   to free captives from prison
   and to release from the dungeon those who sit in darkness."

_____

_____

_____

_____

_____

_____

_____

_____

_____

_____

First Thursday of Advent, December 4, 2008

ISAIAH 53:2-5, 11-12

He had no beauty or majesty to attract us to him,

nothing in his appearance that we should desire him.

He was despised and rejected by men,

a man of sorrows, and familiar with suffering.

Like one from whom men hide their faces

he was despised, and we esteemed him not.

Surely he took up our infirmities

and carried our sorrows,

yet we considered him stricken by God,

smitten by him, and afflicted.

But he was pierced for our transgressions,

he was crushed for our iniquities;

the punishment that brought us peace was upon him,

and by his wounds we are healed.

After the suffering of his soul,

he will see the light of life and be satisfied;

by his knowledge my righteous servant will justify many,

and he will bear their iniquities.

Therefore I will give him a portion among the great,
and he will divide the spoils with the strong,
because he poured out his life unto death,
and was numbered with the transgressors.
For he bore the sin of many,
and made intercession for the transgressors.

_____

_____

_____

_____

_____

_____

_____

_____

_____

_____

_____

_____

_____

_____

First Friday of Advent, December 5, 2008

ISAIAH 61:1-3

The Spirit of the Sovereign LORD is on me,

because the LORD has anointed me

to preach good news to the poor.

He has sent me to bind up the brokenhearted,

to proclaim freedom for the captives

and release from darkness for the prisoners,

to proclaim the year of the LORD's favor

and the day of vengeance of our God,

to comfort all who mourn,

and provide for those who grieve in Zion—
    to bestow on them a crown of beauty
    instead of ashes,
    the oil of gladness
    instead of mourning,
    and a garment of praise
    instead of a spirit of despair.
    They will be called oaks of righteousness,
    a planting of the LORD
    for the display of his splendor.

First Saturday of Advent, December 6, 2008

LUKE 1:26–38

In the sixth month, God sent the angel Gabriel to Nazareth, a town in Galilee, to a virgin pledged to be married to a man named Joseph, a descendant of David. The virgin's name was Mary. The angel went to her and said, "Greetings, you who are highly favored! The Lord is with you."

Mary was greatly troubled at his words and wondered what kind of greeting this might be. But the angel said to her, "Do not be afraid, Mary, you have found favor with God.

You will be with child and give birth to a son, and you are to give him the name Jesus. He will be great and will be called the Son of the Most High. The Lord God will give him the throne of his father David, and he will reign over the house of Jacob forever; his kingdom will never end."

"How will this be," Mary asked the angel, "since I am a virgin?"

The angel answered, "The Holy Spirit will come upon you, and the power of the Most High will overshadow you. So the holy one to be born will be called the Son of God. Even

Elizabeth your relative is going to have a child in her old age, and she who was said to be barren is in her sixth month. For nothing is impossible with God."

"I am the Lord's servant," Mary answered. "May it be to me as you have said." Then the angel left her.

_____

_____

_____

_____

_____

Second Sunday of Advent, December 7, 2008

ISAIAH 11:1-2, 10

A shoot will come up from the stump of Jesus;

  from his roots a Branch will bear fruit.

The Spirit of the LORD will rest on him—

  the Spirit of wisdom and of understanding,

  the Spirit of counsel and of power,

  the Spirit of knowledge and of the fear of

    the LORD—

In that day the Root of Jesse will stand as a banner for the peoples; the nations will rally to him, and his place of rest will be glorious.

_____

_____

_____

_____

_____

_____

_____

_____

_____

_____

Second Monday of Advent, December 8, 2008

MICAH 5:2

"But you, Bethlehem Ephrathah,

though you are small among the clans of Judah,

out of you will come for me

one who will be ruler over Israel,

whose origins are from of old,

from ancient times."

_____

_____

_____

_____

_____

_____

_____

_____

_____

_____

Second Tuesday of Advent, December 9, 2008

ROMANS 15:8-11, 13

For I tell you that Christ has become a servant of the Jews on behalf of God's truth, to confirm the promises made to the patriarchs so that the Gentiles may glorify God for his mercy, as it is written:

"Therefore I will praise you among the Gentiles;
I will sing hymns to your name." Again, it says,
"Rejoice, O Gentiles, with his people." And again,

"Praise the Lord, all you Gentiles,
   and sing praises to him, all you peoples."

May the God of hope fill you with all joy and peace as you trust in him, so that you may overflow with hope by the power of the Holy Spirit.

_____

_____

_____

_____

_____

_____

_____

_____

_____

_____

_____

_____

_____

_____

Second Wednesday of Advent, December 10, 2008

1 PETER 2:6–9

For in Scripture it says:

> *"See, I lay a stone in Zion,*
> *a chosen and precious cornerstone,*
> *and the one who trusts in him*
> *will never be put to shame."*

Now to you who believe, this stone is precious. But to those who do not believe,

"The stone the builders rejected
*   has become the capstone," and,*
"A stone that causes men to stumble
*   and a rock that makes them fall."*
They stumble because they disobey the message—which is also
what they were destined for.

*   But you are a chosen people, a royal priesthood, a holy*
nation, a people belonging to God, that you may declare the
praises of him who called you out of darkness into his
wonderful light.

Second Thursday of Advent, December 11, 2008

ISAIAH 60:1-3

"Arise, shine, for your light has come,

and the glory of the LORD rises upon you.

See, darkness covers the earth

and thick darkness is over the peoples,

but the LORD rises upon you

and his glory appears over you.

Nations will come to your light,

and kings to the brightness of your dawn."

_____

_____

_____

_____

_____

_____

_____

_____

_____

_____

Second Friday of Advent, December 12, 2008

JOHN 3:16

For God so loved the world that he gave his one and only Son, that whoever believes in him shall not perish but have eternal life.

_____

_____

_____

_____

_____

_____

_____

_____

_____

_____

_____

Second Saturday of Advent, December 13, 2008

LUKE 2:8-20

And there were shepherds living out in the fields nearby, keeping watch over their flocks at night. An angel of the Lord appeared to them, and the glory of the Lord shone around them, and they were terrified. But the angel said to them, "Do not be afraid. I bring you good news of great joy that will be for all the people. Today in the town of David a Savior has been born to you; he is Christ the Lord. This will be a sign to you: You will find a baby wrapped in cloths and lying in a manger."

Suddenly a great company of the heavenly host appeared with the angel, praising God and saying,

"Glory to God in the highest,
and on earth peace to men on whom his
favor rests."

When the angels had left them and gone into heaven, the shepherds said to one another, "Let's go to Bethlehem and see this thing that has happened, which the Lord has told us about."

So they hurried off and found Mary and Joseph, and the baby, who was lying in the manger. When they had seen him, they spread the word concerning what had been told them about this child, and all who heard it were amazed at what the shepherds said to them. But Mary treasured up all these things and pondered them in her heart. The shepherds returned, glorifying and praising God for all the things they had heard and seen, which were just as they had been told.

_____

_____

_____

_____

_____

_____

_____

_____

_____

Third Sunday of Advent, December 14, 2008

MATTHEW 2:10-11

When they saw the star, they were overjoyed. On coming to the house, they saw the child with his mother Mary, and they bowed down and worshiped him. Then they opened their treasures and presented him with gifts of gold and of incense and of myrrh.

_____

_____

_____

_____

_____

_____

_____

_____

_____

_____

Third Monday of Advent, December 15, 2008
LUKE 2:7

*And she gave birth to her firstborn, a son. She wrapped him in
cloths and placed him in a manger, because there was no room
for them in the inn.*

_____

_____

_____

_____

_____

_____

_____

_____

_____

_____

Third Tuesday of Advent, December 16, 2008

MATTHEW 1:23

"The virgin will be with child and will give birth to a son, and they will call him Immanuel"–which means, "God with us."

_____

_____

_____

_____

_____

Third Wednesday of Advent, December 17, 2008

MARK 1:15

"The time has come," he said. "The kingdom of God is near. Repent and believe the good news!"

_____

_____

_____

_____

_____

_____

Third Thursday of Advent, December 18, 2008

ISAIAH 52:7, 9-10

How beautiful on the mountains

are the feet of those who bring good news,

who proclaim peace,

who bring good tidings,

who proclaim salvation,

who say to Zion,

"Your God reigns!"

Burst into songs of joy together,

you ruins of Jerusalem,

for the LORD has comforted his people,

he has redeemed Jerusalem.

The LORD will lay bare his holy arm

in the sight of all the nations,

and all the ends of the earth will see

the salvation of our God.

_____

_____

_____

_____

_____

_____

_____

_____

_____

_____

_____

_____

_____

Third Friday of Advent, December 19, 2008

JOHN 1:4-5

In him was life, and that life was the light of men. The light shines in the darkness, but the darkness has not understood it.

_____

_____

_____

_____

_____

_____

Third Saturday of Advent, December 20, 2008

ZEPHANIAH 3:14-17

Sing, O Daughter of Zion;

shout aloud, O Israel!

Be glad and rejoice with all your heart,

O Daughter of Jerusalem!

The LORD has taken away your punishment,

he has turned back your enemy.

The LORD, the King of Israel, is with you;

never again will you fear any harm.

On that day they will say to Jerusalem,
"Do not fear, O Zion;
do not let your hands hang limp.
The LORD your God is with you,
he is mighty to save.
He will take great delight in you,
he will quiet you with his love,
he will rejoice over you with singing."

_____

_____

Fourth Sunday of Advent, December 21, 2008

MALACHI 3:1-2

"See, I will send my messenger, who will prepare the way before me. Then suddenly the Lord you are seeking will come to his temple; the messenger of the covenant, whom you desire, will come," says the Lord Almighty.

But who can endure the day of his coming? Who can stand when he appears? For he will be like a refiner's fire or a launderer's soap.

Fourth Monday of Advent, December 22, 2008

ISAIAH 40:3, 5

A voice of one calling:

"In the desert prepare

the way for the LORD;

make straight in the wilderness

a highway for our God.

And the glory of the LORD will be revealed,

and all mankind together will see it.

For the mouth of the LORD has spoken."

_____

_____

_____

_____

_____

_____

_____

_____

_____

Fourth Tuesday of Advent, December 23, 2008

TITUS 2:11-14

For the grace of God that brings salvation has appeared to all men. It teaches us to say "No" to ungodliness and worldly passions, and to live self-controlled, upright and godly lives in this present age, while we wait for the blessed hope—the glorious appearing of our great God and Savior, Jesus Christ, who gave himself for us to redeem us from all wickedness and to purify for himself a people that are his very own, eager to do what is good.

Fourth Wednesday of Advent, Christmas Eve, December 24, 2008

JOHN 1:10-14

He was in the world, and though the world was made through him, the world did not recognize him. He came to that which was his own, but his own did not receive him. Yet to all who received him, to those who believed in his name, he gave the right to become children of God—children born not of natural descent, nor of human decision or a husband's will, but born of God.

The Word became flesh and made his dwelling among us. We have seen his glory, the glory of the One and Only, who came from the Father, full of grace and truth.

_____

_____

_____

_____

_____

_____

_____

_____

_____

_____

_____

_____

_____

_____

_____

_____

_____

_____

ABOUT THE AUTHOR

Dr. Charles R. Swindoll is senior pastor of Stonebriar Community Church, chancellor of Dallas Theological Seminary, and the Bible teacher on the internationally syndicated radio program *Insight for Living*. He has written more than thirty best-selling books, such as *Strengthening Your Grip, Laugh Again, The Grace Awakening,* and the million-selling *Great Lives from God's Word* series. Chuck and his wife, Cynthia, live in Frisco, Texas.